Disney · PIXAR

BRAVE

STICKER SCENE

PaRragon

Bath · New York · Singapore · Hong Kong · Cologne · Delhi
Melbourne · Amsterdam · Johannesburg · Auckland · Shenzhen

Merida is a fiery, redheaded princess. Raised in a land rich with legends, she is expected to be a traditional queen just like her mother.

However, Merida is often found on her trusty horse, Angus, riding through the forests of DunBroch, wind in her hair and a bow and arrow in her hand!

Use your stickers to show Merida and Angus on a great adventure!

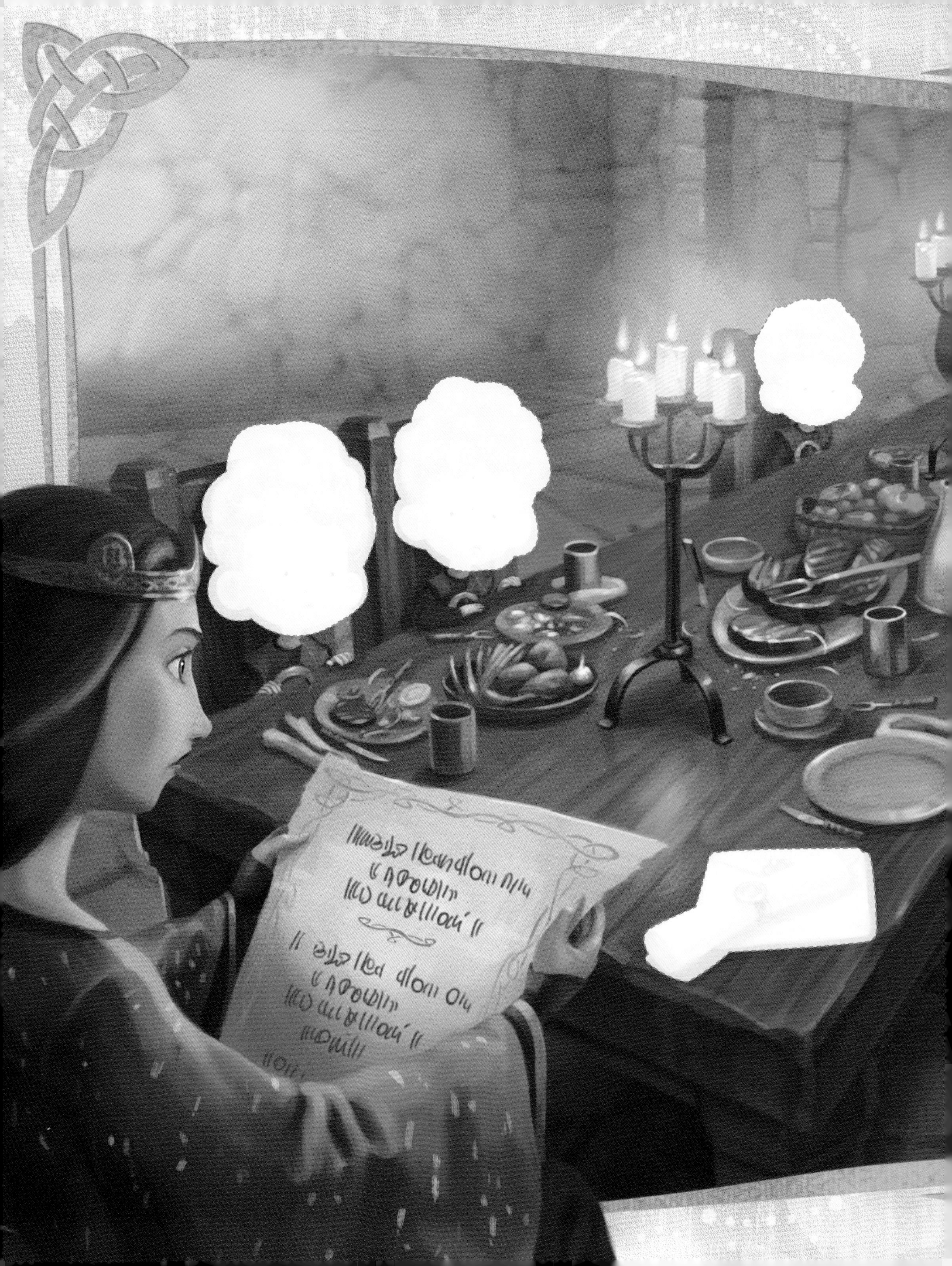

Merida's father and brothers enjoy her adventures but her mother thinks she needs to act more like a princess.

Queen Elinor expects Merida to marry one of the lords' sons, securing peace in the kingdom. But Merida is angry, she's happy with her life.

Use your stickers to complete this scene of the royal family.

BEAR BATTLE

"LEGENDS ARE LESSONS,
THEY RING WITH TRUTHS."

©Disney/Pixar

Forest Pursuit

"A PRINCESS ENJOYS ELEGANT PURSUITS."

©Disney/Pixar

Family Dinner

"I SUPPOSE A PRINCESS JUST DOES WHAT SHE'S TOLD!"

©Disney/Pixar

ARCHERY COMPETITION

"I'LL BE SHOOTING FOR MY OWN HAND!"

WITCH'S COTTAGE

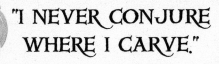

"I NEVER CONJURE WHERE I CARVE."

FAMILY REUNION

"MEND THE BOND
TORN BY PRIDE."

The lords' sons compete in an archery competition, to win Merida's hand.

When Merida displays her superior archery talents, Queen Elinor is furious and fears the visiting clans will declare war. She punishes Merida.

Use your stickers to show Merida's victory.

In her anger Merida slashes the family tapestry and storms out.

She rides Angus deep into the forest until she comes across some magical will o' the wisps. They lead her to a strange cottage belonging to a witch. The witch grants Merida one spell to help change her destiny.

Use your stickers to show the witch making a magical cake.

Merida gives the cake to her mother thinking it will make her change her mind about the marriage. But it turns her into a giant bear!

Hearing of a monster bear in the area, King Fergus and the lords set off on a hunt.

Use your stickers to show the heroic princess protecting her mum from the hunters.

Merida repairs the torn tapestry and saves her mother.
The spell is broken!

Use your stickers to show the royal family reunited
in this happy ending!